I.S.B.N. 0 85079 132 4

KT-211-150

GILES

SUNDAY EXPRESS & DAILY EXPRESS
CARTOONS

Thirty-seventh Series

AN EXPRESS BOOKS PUBLICATION

£1.60

INTRODUCTION

by

Sir JOHN

BETJEMAN

Poet Laureate

The subtle humour of Giles cartoons are a gentle reflection of the absurdities of our age.

I am very honoured to have been the subject of a cartoon from the past, loved by Giles, depicting a workman climbing from his demolition machine saying to his foreman: ''I've just knocked down John Betjeman.'' It makes me very glad that I should be singled out as a public monument due for demolition, that puts me in the top class, architecturally at least.

I am delighted to endorse yet another Giles annual.

John Betjeman

"I appreciate the Queen has had more than her share for one week, but at least she hasn't got to put up with you lot on holiday for six-and-a-half"

Daily Express, July 22nd, 1982

"The accused then said: 'How about a couple to take home for the wife?' Thereby committing an act of bribery and corruption"

Sunday Express, July 25th, 1982

"All we need now is to discover that Willie Whitelaw is on the board of Gay News"

Daily Express, July 27th, 1982

"It would not only cost half the price to build in Japan—it would be half the bloody mess!"

Daily Express, July 29th, 1982

"That man we paid £10 a head to take us across—I suppose this is his boat?"

Sunday Express, August 1st, 1982

"We're sticking to the old routine—look what happened to Runcie last week when he tried talking peace"

Daily Express, August 3rd, 1982

"I'm not slaving hard all day just for her to teach kids to throw them at Cabinet Ministers"

Daily Express, August 5th, 1982

"Count me out, boys—thanks to my wife's adoration of the Princess of Wales"

Sunday Express, August 8th, 1982

"You're wasting your time, Chaps—he's only giving her the kiss of life"

(There were complaints this week about too much sex on the beaches)

Daily Express, August 10th, 1982

"Something wrong with this strike—I'm working twice as hard as I do normally"

Daily Express, August 12th, 1982

"Before I bop him one—come and see what one of mine has made out of his emergency paper sheets"

Sunday Express, August 15th, 1982

"There are those who may well ask why you should suddenly decide that you need £5 at 2 o'clock in the morning"

Daily Express, August 17th, 1982

"Try me on the option of a 'oliday in Balmoral or bringing in the 'arvest 'ome"

(Capt. Mark Phillips was charged with holidaying during harvest)

Daily Express, August 19th, 1982

"If he's right, some of your flock will end up as roast lamb"

Sunday Express, August 22nd, 1982

"Get out there and I want a good clean fight—keep your punches up and no hitting above the belt"

Daily Express, August 24th, 1982

"My wife says if Mrs Thatcher can be in and out of hospital in one day and back at work the next, so can I"

Daily Express, August 26th, 1982

"It's daddy—he went to the carnival dressed as Buzby—he's now in the Intensive Care Unit where his condition is as well as can be expected"

(Phone charges went up yet again this week)

Sunday Express, August 29th, 1982

"Your Prince asked for it when he said he got to know about the Red Light areas while in the Navy"

Daily Express, August 31st, 1982

"How do you get in touch with the people who banned those video horror films?"

Daily Express, September 2nd, 1982

"Your son has been claiming social security benefits for him and 146 friends all residing in abject poverty at this address"

Sunday Express, September 5th, 1982

"My Prog has sure made me young at heart this week—all the kids back at school and the old man at the Brighton TUC Conference"

Daily Express, September 7th, 1982

"Petrol up another 5p—don't go down to the pub in the Rolls, dear, or *they'll* all be hollering for a rise"

Sunday Express, September 12th, 1982

"There are enough sitting down for meals in this house without your four jury bodyguards"

(At the Old Bailey a jury was given 24 hour police protection)

Daily Express, September 14th, 1982

"They're going to report you for being late and calling them all those rude names"

Daily Express, September 16th, 1982

"Roger brought you a little present from the Falklands, Mummy, but he says there was absolutely nothing in the shops"

Sunday Express, September 19th, 1982

"If anyone hollers 'Emergency' Gawd help you when I get back!"

Daily Express, September 21st, 1982

"All my life I've listened to talk about the 'Good old days.' The way things are going I reckon we're going to get a chance to sample them"

"It's a summons from a burglar who broke in and stole half a bottle of Grandma's home-made wine
and has never been the same since"

Sunday Express, September 26th, 1982

"Meet the latest members of the family—from today bats become a protected species"

Daily Express, September 28th, 1982

"I suppose you'll always get one determined to rise above the common herd"

Daily Express, September 30th, 1982

"Mum, how many Centenary Telegrams has Grandma had from the Queen?"

Sunday Express, October 3rd, 1982

"Do you think you could manage to lift his Teddy off the floor for him?"

Daily Express, October 7th, 1982

"I don't think mother feels 'A bit of all right' becomes a lady who after all could be on the short list for the throne"

Sunday Express, October 10th, 1982

"The Mary Rose woodwork being in good order after 437 years under water we may assume your coffee table has a lifespan of 10 minutes"

Daily Express, October 12th, 1982

"You're jumping the gun, Romeo—Selina Scott doesn't start breakfast TV until next year"

Daily Express, October 14th, 1982

"Anything that gets in as late as him I'd flog to British Rail"

Sunday Express, October 17th, 1982

"It's all very well psychiatrists advising lock 'em in the loo when they're naughty—they don't have a grandma in there reading the racing page"

Daily Express, October 19th, 1982

"I'm suddenly developing a total allergy to your mother running on about the wonderful new Ford Sierra"

Daily Express, October 21st, 1982

"The ref's blown for offside—you can tell by the bubbles"

Sunday Express, October 24th, 1982

"You're in it either way, corporal—Daddy doesn't seem very happy, and your little Goose Green Gertie appears to be on the banned list"

Daily Express, October 26th, 1982

"I suggest a small increase in salary for Ivy might keep the Industrial Tribunal off our backs, M'Lady"

Sunday Express, October 31st, 1982

"Let me get this right—you want to come in an hour later because of Breakfast TV and knock off an hour earlier to see Channel 4?"

Daily Express, November 2nd, 1982

"Says she pops in every afternoon for a nap in the State Coach—and played hell because the Queen borrowed it yesterday"

Daily Express, November 4th, 1982

"Well, that's taken care of your ambulance—telling them you knew they'd have to give way in the end"

Sunday Express, November 7th, 1982

"What's the betting we end up helping the Argentines to get rid of their Government, the Russians, and the Americans"

Daily Express, November 9th, 1982

"Cut! We all saw her in the papers, but Angela Rippon wasn't playing a Herald Angel in our Christmas play"

Daily Express, November 11th, 1982

"Many more stops for our driver to say hullo to his French connections and our Beaujolais Nouveau
will be Beaujolais Vintage"

Sunday Express, November 14th, 1982

"By the way—where did we leave the snow plough last year?"

Daily Express, November 16th, 1982

"I'd skip the 'Good morning, Miss World'. She's just worked out what she's not going to get in the way of pensions"

Daily Express, November 18th, 1982

"Who's going to tell our oil tycoon those two Britoil shares she bought are going to be worth peanuts by next week."

Sunday Express, November 21st, 1982

"Missile Command to invaders: Hop it, we're closed!"

Daily Express, November 23rd, 1982

"Watch 'im Vera"

Daily Express, November 25th, 1982

"Princess Diana is being absolutely selfish not letting her baby have a dummy"

Sunday Express, November 28th, 1982

"Who the 'ell's been sleeping in my bed?" said Father Bear; "That bleeding little nymphomaniac, Goldie Locks," wagered Mummy Bear. "Why, the two-timing, double-crossing no-good," murmured Baby Bear. Then they all switched over to Channel 2

(There was uproar in the Commons about cleaning up children's TV)

Daily Express, December 2nd, 1982

"It might keep your head warm, but that won't stop the neighbours identifying us with the KGB"

Sunday Express, December 5th, 1982

"Vera—if I've got any tears to shed this morning I give you my written guarantee right now they're not for E.T."

Daily Express, December 9th, 1982

"Somebody kindly inform the lady that we are not muggers"

Sunday Express, December 12th, 1982

"You shouldn't have told them you thought it was a bloody good film—they've put you on mucking out all Christmas"

(A not very complimentary documentary about racehorse owners appeared on TV)

Daily Express, December 14th, 1982

"Doris! You didn't tell me you'd taken a part-time job for Christmas"

Daily Express, December 16th, 1982

"You want to watch the jokes—it's going to take them a little time to settle down after losing their claim"

Sunday Express, December 19th, 1982

"You say the lady kissed your head under the mistletoe thereby causing you sexual harassment?"

Daily Express, December 21st, 1982

"It's the plumber we ordered in August—he can come and do the drain this afternoon"

Daily Express, December 24th, 1982

"Yes, we had a nice Christmas—we all sang carols then Grandma killed off two or three thousand Space Invaders on her video computer"

Daily Express, December 28th, 1982

"You're not sending him back to Harridges to change them all on his own"

Daily Express, December 30th, 1982

"My Happy New Year will begin when the decorations and the last mince pie are down and not before"

Sunday Express, January 2nd, 1983

"Remember last night? 1983 is going to be different — we're all going to live like they do in The Good Life on TV"

Daily Express, January 4th, 1983

"Madam, because there happens to be nobody aboard, it does not mean this ship is abandoned,
and what you have there is not salvage—it's loot"

Daily Express, January 6th, 1983

"If our fishermen say they can't make a living from our waters how come the Danes are so keen to come here?"

Sunday Express, January 9th, 1983

"Galley slave to Admiral of the Fleet . . . breakfast!"

Daily Express, January 11th, 1983

"Stop practising Teasy Weasy—she's gone back"

Daily Express, January 13th, 1983

"M.P's are not the only ones having trouble with their gates"

(Despite 3 million unemployed M.P. cannot get gate repaired)

Sunday Express, January 16th, 1983

"You'll have to start getting to bed earlier to get down in time to see your Debbie and Selina"

Daily Express, January 18th, 1983

"I appreciate the Islanders' wishes are paramount . . . I simply said I wish it wasn't me
who makes bloody sure they are"

Daily Express, January 20th, 1983

"We've got to sign an agreement that in the event of a future water shortage no way will they have to share a bath with Grandma"

Sunday Express, January 23rd, 1983

"Morning, Harry—you're taking over the Leeds football fan control and the water strike sewerage protection brigades"

Daily Express, January 25th, 1983

"Daddy, the man next door's syphoning your bath water to clean his car"

Daily Express, January 27th, 1983

"Here comes one of 'em without a seatbelt—cover me, I'm going in"

Sunday Express, January 30th, 1983

"Dad, I've just counted up—we've got six more people than we've got in the family"

Daily Express, February 1st, 1983

"That's my missus—thanks to this Mike Baldwin in Coronation Street she thinks I might be at it"

Daily Express, February 3rd, 1983

"If he don't agree to our wage claim I doubt if he'll be home in time for his breakfast telly"

Sunday Express, February 6th, 1983

"They jump up and down to get hot, we melt the snow on their heads, and it sells retail at 10p a pint"

Daily Express, February 8th, 1983

"Of course everybody's late—you were so happy on your No Smoking Day you fired 'em all"

Daily Express, February 10th, 1983

"Penelope, Miss Ringboane-Smythe wants you to join the search party—someone's stolen Pegasus"

(Shergar the famous racehorse was kidnapped this week)

Sunday Express, February 13th, 1983

"Good morning, Porky . . . O symbol of Peace and Tranquillity"

Daily Express, February 15th, 1983

"I took one to bits to prove it was all British, but she found the hands were made in Taiwan"

Daily Express, February 17th, 1983

"The next time you bring your tank home to show mummy, be a good chap and keep it off the lawn"
(Sapper borrows tank for weekend)

Sunday Express, February 20th, 1983

"You can use the path today—they've put me on this low-calorie diet for dogs"

Daily Express, February 22nd, 1983

"The boys say they're not going to waste their talents kicking people's heads in at football
if they're not going to be on television"

Sunday Express, February 27th, 1983

"The Brits bought Manhattan for half what you just paid for that flag"

Daily Express, March 1st, 1983

"Selina's four letter word will be nothing compared with Dad's when he knows Mum's still hanging on the phone to complain to the BBC"

Daily Express, March 3rd, 1983

"That was very rude to tell aunty that a couple of weeks at the coalface would make her think differently about the miners' strike"

Sunday Express, March 6th, 1983

"Don't disturb Butch—he's calling that little Jack Russell who answers telephones"

(Dog answers phone when owner's out)

Daily Express, March 10th, 1983

"Who suggested we got Mother outdoor plants for Mothering Sunday?"

Sunday Express, March 13th, 1983

(Prince Charles, Princess Diana and Prince William arrived in Australia)

Daily Express, March 12th, 1983

"I don't think Grandma likes your new boyfriend calling her a fair dinkum pom — her knuckles keep going white"

Sunday Express, March 27th, 1983

"Daily Express 'witty guides to gardening for the total ignoramus' won't make me like it more than I do already"

Daily Express, March 29th, 1983

"You never know with frogs—any one of 'em could be His Royal Highness"

Daily Express, March 31st, 1983

"Any political party who bans horses as well as fox hunting will get my vote"

Sunday Express, April 3rd, 1983

"I didn't say that our Charlie pushing the boat out means he's connected with the £7m robbery—
I simply said it makes him highly suspect"

Daily Express, April 7th, 1983

"The man who takes the money says you've forgotten his tip!"

Sunday Express, April 10th, 1983

"What's the betting Aintree doesn't see a penny of it?"

Daily Express, April 12th, 1983

"It's your dad—he's invited them to hold their duel on our lawn"

Daily Express, April 14th, 1983

"Hold it! If we're entering a team and I'm in charge of you, you're wearing these"

Sunday Express, April 17th, 1983

"On the other hand I can't find a ruling that says if you merge two teams you can't play twenty two men"

Daily Express, April 19th, 1983

" 'Good Morning Britain' is much more natural now—my parents always have a bloody good row for breakfast"

Daily Express, April 21st, 1983

"Oh 'eck—the wives have found out Robert Maxwell's merged us with a women's football team"

Sunday Express, April 24th, 1983

"I didn't SAY she wrote them—I only said she COULD have written them"

Daily Express, April 26th, 1983

"Sorry to butt in again, M'am, but would you mind signing 'By Appointment' on my new punk disc?"

Daily Express, April 28th, 1983

"If the Queen Mother's car made you late for lunch, you'd better write and ask Her to use another way home in future"

(Edward Heath complained royal car held him up)

Sunday Express, May 1st, 1983

"High-rise May Pole Dancers vs Gas Works Street Morris Dancers — May Day competition"

Daily Express, May 3rd, 1983

"The zoo lady said they pong a little at first, but after you get to know them, they are really quite appealing"

Daily Express, May 5th, 1983

"Some of these entries in your diary had better be fakes, my lady"

Hitler's diaries were exposed as fakes

Sunday Express, May 8th, 1983

"Darling, they've just announced on the radio the Election date is June the ninth!"

Daily Express, May 10th, 1983

"Would you like to handle this one? 'How come they've fixed the election date but the prices haven't come down?' "

Daily Express, May 12th, 1983

"Dad this is Vince—he's torn between Mrs Thatcher, Andropov and Screaming Lord Sutch"

Sunday Express, May 15th, 1983

"We was always taught to spell it 'h-a-n-g-e-d'"

Daily Express, May 19th, 1983

"Cooper! Be a good chap and check with her Ladyship if we're a two-car family"

Sunday Express, May 22nd, 1983

"They want to know if they can go fishing in your barn"

Daily Express, May 24th, 1983

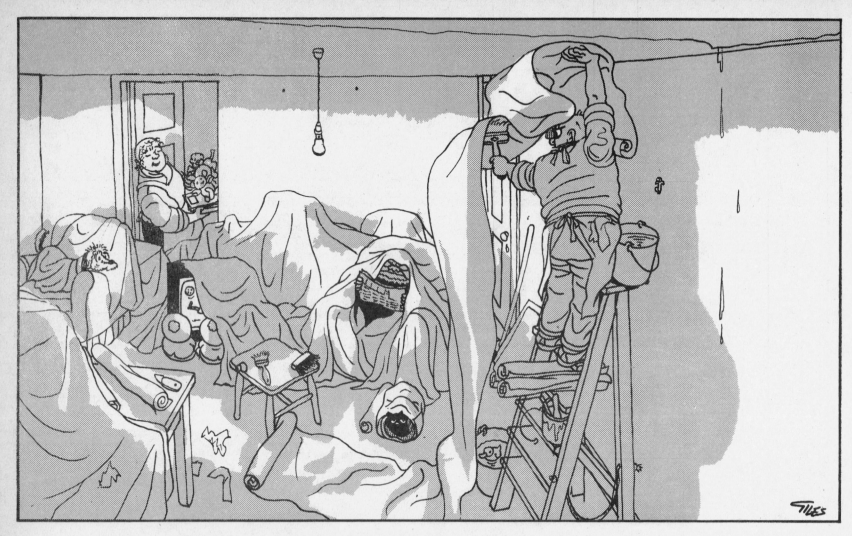

"Bad luck one of your Cup finals falling on the day you promised to do the ceiling"

Daily Express, May 26th, 1983

"Nurse, at the risk of a full spread blasting in Nursing Times—I think you're positively ravishing"

Sunday Express, May 29th, 1983

"This will cheer you up—the Scout gives the same odds for you being in the first ten as he gives Ken Livingstone being Home Secretary in a Thatcher Government"

Daily Express, May 31st, 1983

"That was unfortunate, Willie—they're all in the feeding stuff business"

Daily Express, June 2nd, 1983

"Vicar's got a tip off his little finger, does that mean he's having a wild affair with Shirley MacLaine?"

(Clue to Shirley MacLaine's mystery M.P. lover — fingertip missing)

Sunday Express, June 5th, 1983

"After lugging her backwards and forwards to the shops for a month, the old bag had better vote for me!"

Daily Express, June 7th, 1983

"The scientists are right . . . trees CAN talk. This one just said he'd be glad if you'd take this rubbish off him when you come back from the polls"

Daily Express, June 9th, 1983